周海生

Zhōu Hǎishēng

The Misadventures of Zhou Haisheng

John Pasden and Jared Turner

Mandarin Companion

Chinese Graded Readers

Published by Mind Spark Press LLC Shanghai, China

Mandarin Companion is a trademark of Mind Spark Press LLC.

Copyright © Mind Spark Press LLC, 2019

For information about educational or bulk purchases, please contact Mind Spark Press at BUSINESS@MANDARINCOMPANION.COM.

Instructor and learner resources and traditional Chinese editions of the Mandarin Companion series are available at WWW.MANDARINCOMPANION.COM.

First paperback print edition 2019

Library of Congress Cataloging-in-Publication Data The Misadventures of Zhou Haisheng: Mandarin Companion Graded Readers: Breakthrough Level, Simplified Chinese Edition / John Pasden and Jared Turner; [edited by] John Pasden, Chen Shishuang, Li Jiong, Ma Lihua Shanghai, China: Mind Spark Press LLC, 2019 Library of Congress Control Number: 2019905065

ISBN: 9781941875391 (Paperback)
ISBN: 9781941875414 (Paperback/traditional ch)
ISBN: 9781941875407 (ebook)
ISBN: 9781941875421 (ebook/traditional ch)

MCID: TFH20220818T094512

What Graded Readers can do for you

Welcome to Mandarin Companion!

We've worked hard to create enjoyable stories that can help you build confidence and competence and get better at Chinese–at the right level for you.

Our graded readers have controlled and simplified language that allows you to bring together the language you've learned so far and absorb how words work naturally together. Research suggests that learners need to "encounter" a word 10-30 times before truly learning it. Graded readers provide the repetition that you need to develop fluency NOW at your level.

In the next section, you can take an assessment and discover if this is the right level for you. We also explain how it won't just improve your Chinese skills but will have a wide range of benefits, from better test scores to increased confidence.

We hope you enjoy our books, and best of luck with your studies. Jared and John

Frequently Asked Questions

Do you have versions with pinyin over the characters?

No. Although this method is common for native Chinese learners, research and experience show it distracts a second language learner and slows down their ability to learn the characters. If you require pinyin to read most of the characters at this level, you should read something easier.

Is there an English translation of the story?

No. Research and experience show that an English translation will slow down the development of your Chinese language learning skills.

Is this the right level for me?

Let's find out. Open to a story page with characters and start reading. Keep track of the number of characters you *don't* know but don't count any key words you don't know. If there are more than 5 unknown characters on that page, you may want to consider working on your basic character recognition before attempting a graded reader. If the unknown characters are fewer than 5, then this book is likely at your level! If you find that you know all the characters, you may be ready for a higher level. However, even if you know all the characters but are reading slowly, you should consider building reading speed before moving up a level.

How do you decide which characters to include at each level?

Each level includes a core set of characters based on our extensive analysis of the most common characters and words taught to and used by those learning Chinese as a second language. All books at each level are based on the same core set and they can be read in any order.

What to expect in a Breakthrough book?

It's important that you read at the level that is right for you. Check out the next page to learn more about Extensive Reading and how we use that in graded readers to support the learning of Chinese by just enjoying a good story.

Books in our Breakthrough Level like this one:

- Include a core set of 150 Chinese words and characters learners are most likely to know.
- Are about 5,000 characters in length
- Use level appropriate grammar

- Include pinyin and a translation of words and characters you are not expected to know at this level
- Include a glossary at the back of book
- Include proper nouns that are underlined

What is Extensive Reading?

It will improve test scores, your reading speed and comprehension, speaking, listening and writing skills. You'll pick up grammar naturally, you'll begin understanding in Chinese, your confidence will improve, and you'll enjoy learning the language.

Graded Readers are based on science that is backed by mountains of research and proven by learners all over the world. They are founded on the theories of Extensive Reading and Comprehensible Input.

Extensive Reading is reading at a level where you can understand almost all of what you are reading (ideally 98%) at a comfortable speed, as opposed to stumbling through dense paragraphs word by word.

When you read extensively, you'll understand most of the words and find yourself fully engaged with the story.

	Reading Pain	Intensive Reading	Extensive Reading
READING LEVEL:			
COMPREHENSION:	90%	98%	100%

Reading at 98% comprehension is the sweet spot to max out your learning gains. You do still learn at the Intensive Reading level (90–98%), but the closer you are to the Extensive level, the faster your progress.

No one should be reading below a 90% comprehension level.

It's called Reading Pain for a reason. You spend so much time in a dictionary and after 30 painful minutes on ONE paragraph, you're not even sure what you've just read!

If you want to know more, check out our website
www.mandarincompanion.com

Table of Contents

Story Notes

A sizable portion of China's large cities are home to those who have come to pursue opportunities and dreams in the big city. This story captures the common tale of a young family trying to carve out a life in Shanghai while trying to provide educational opportunities for their young son. These dynamics bring diversity and, specifically for this tale, culinary variety to major cities throughout China.

The childhood escapades of young Zhou Haisheng, specifically life events that put him on the path to one day open his own restaurant, tie into the larger "Mandarin Companion Universe." If you're curious how things turn out for him after reading this origin story, prepare to read *Emma*, a Mandarin Companion Level 1 story.

Character Adaptations

The following is a list of the characters from this Chinese story followed by their corresponding English names from John Pasden and Jared Turner's original story. The names below are not translations; they are new Chinese names used for the Chinese versions of the original characters. Think of them as all-new characters in a Chinese story.

周海生 (Zhōu Hǎishēng) – Zhou Haisheng
老周 (Lǎo Zhōu) – Mr. Zhou
周太太 (Zhōu Tàitai) – Mrs. Zhou
錢太太 (Qián Tàitai) – Mrs. Qian
馬老師 (Mǎ Lǎoshī) – Ms. Ma

Cast of Characters

周海生
(Zhōu Hǎishēng)

老周
(Lǎo Zhōu)

周太太
(Zhōu Tàitai)

錢太太
(Qián Tàitai)

馬老師
(Mǎ Lǎoshī)

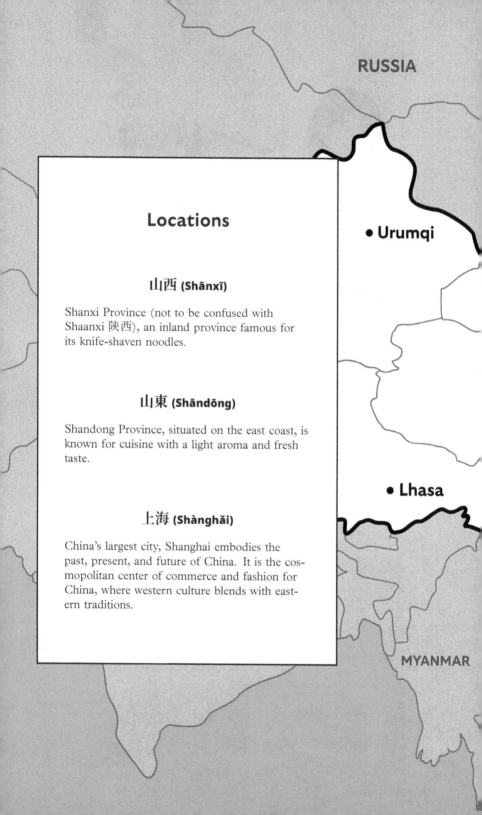

RUSSIA

• Urumqi

Locations

山西 (Shānxī)

Shanxi Province (not to be confused with Shaanxi 陕西), an inland province famous for its knife-shaven noodles.

山東 (Shāndōng)

Shandong Province, situated on the east coast, is known for cuisine with a light aroma and fresh taste.

• Lhasa

上海 (Shànghǎi)

China's largest city, Shanghai embodies the past, present, and future of China. It is the cosmopolitan center of commerce and fashion for China, where western culture blends with eastern traditions.

MYANMAR

做面

上學了

周海生今年八歲，他的爸爸叫老
周。老周做的菜很好吃，在上海開了
一家飯店，叫"周家飯店"。飯店不大，
可是每天都有很多人。飯店裡有飯，
有面，還有很多菜。

老周的老家在山西。老周和 他 的

1　歲 (suì) *mw.* years old
2　叫 (jiào) *v.* to be called, to call; to tell (someone to do something)
3　好吃 (hǎochī) *adj.* tasty
4　家 (jiā) *mw.* measure word for shops
5　飯店 (fàndiàn) *n.* restaurant
6　可是 (kěshì) *conj.* but
7　還 (hái) *adv.* still
8　老家 (lǎojiā) *n.* hometown

太太來上海開了這家飯店。兒子出生
　9　　　　　　　　4　　5　　　　10　　11

在上海，名字叫周海生。
　　　　　12　2

　　海生小的時候，每天都和爸爸媽
　　　　　　13

媽一起去飯店。他們一家人每天都
　　14　　5　　　　　　　　15

9　太太 (tàitai) *n.* wife, lady, Mrs.

10　兒子 (érzi) *n.* son

11　出生 (chūshēng) *v.* to be born

12　名字 (míngzi) *n.* name

13　的時候 (de shíhou) *phrase* when…

14　一起 (yīqǐ) *adv.* together

15　一家人 (yī jiā rén) *phrase* the whole family

在飯店吃飯，每天都很晚關門回家。

可以說，飯店是海生的第二個家。

　　來"周家飯店"吃飯的人都很喜

歡海生，喜歡和他說話。海生七歲生

日的時候，老周的太太對老周說："兒

子都這麼大了，不能天天都在飯店裡，

可以去上學了。"老周聽了點點頭。

　　周太太小時候沒　有上學，可是她

16　晚 (wǎn) *adj.* late

17　關門 (guānmén) *vo.* to close shop, to close a door

18　回家 (huíjiā) *vo.* to go home

19　喜歡 (xǐhuan) *v.* to like

20　說話 (shuōhuà) *vo.* to speak (words), to talk

21　生日 (shēngrì) *n.* birthday

22　這麼 (zhème) *adv.* so···

23　天天 (tiāntiān) *adv.* every day

24　上學 (shàngxué) *vo.* to start school, to go to school

25　聽 (tīng) *v.* to listen (to)

26　點點頭 (diǎndian tóu) *phrase* to (briefly) nod one's head

27　小時候 (xiǎo shíhou) *phrase* when one was little

兒子能上學，她很開心。

周海生每天中午不回家吃飯，周太太每天早上都會做吃的，那是海生的午飯。

海生喜歡上學，上學以後，他有了很多朋友。他喜歡和朋友們在一起吃午飯，吃完飯以後，他們還能一起寫字。

每天下午四點多，海生都會回到

---

28 開心 (kāixīn) *adj.* happy

29 中午 (zhōngwǔ) *n.* noon

30 早上 (zǎoshang) *tn.* morning

31 吃的 (chī de) *n.* food

32 午飯 (wǔfàn) *n.* lunch

33 以後 (yǐhòu) *adv.* after; later, in the future

34 在一起 (zài yīqǐ) *phrase* to be together

35 吃完 (chī wán) *vc.* to finish eating

飯店。周太太會問兒子，今天又學了

什麼東西。要是飯店沒人來吃飯，她

會看海生寫字。

---

36 又 (yòu) *adv.* again

37 東西 (dōngxi) *n.* thing(s), stuff

38 要是 (yàoshi) *conj.* if

海生想："怎麼會關門呢？還不到
五點。"

海生又說："媽媽，我回來了！"沒
有人說話。

---

43 怎麼會 (zěnme huì) *phrase* how could   **44** 回來 (huílai) *vc.* to come back

"爸爸，我朋友想吃麵。"還是沒有
人說話。

老周和周太太都不在，飯店裡一個
人也沒有，可是店門也沒關好。

海生的朋友看看他，說："你爸爸
不在，我明天再來吃麵吧。"

"不行，我們都來了，吃吧!"海生
說，"我爸爸不在，我來給你做。"說
完，海生對朋友笑笑。

---

45 還是 (háishi) *conj., adv.* still

46 看看 (kànkan) *v.* to take a look

47 再 (zài) *adv.* again (in the future)

48 不行 (bù xíng) *phrase* not OK

49 說完 (shuō wán) *vc.* to finish speaking

50 笑 (xiào) *v.* to laugh, to smile

"你也會做面?"朋友也笑笑,"我要看看你是怎麼做的。"

"我小時候天天看我爸爸做面,也跟他學了一點。"海生一邊跟朋友說話,一邊做面。面做完了以後,他和朋友都很開心。

"怎麼樣?好吃嗎?"海生一邊吃,一邊問朋友。

"好吃,太好吃了!"

"那你多吃點!"海生開心地說。

---

51 做面 (zuò miàn) *vo.* to make noodles   52 怎麼 (zěnme) *adv.* how

"謝謝，我吃完了。"朋友很開心，"可

是，我沒有錢。多少錢？我明天給

你。"

"今天的面不要錢。"海生說完以後

他們都笑了。

這時候，來了幾個人，想吃飯和

菜。

"我爸爸媽媽出去了，我不會做菜。

你們晚上再來吧。"海生對那幾個人

說。

---

53 這時候 (zhè shíhou) *phrase* at this time

54 出去 (chūqu) *vc.* to go out

55 做菜 (zuòcài) *vo.* to cook food

56 晚上 (wǎnshang) *tn.* evening

"那你們吃的是什麼？"一個男人一邊笑一邊問。

"面，他做的。"海生的朋友說。

"好吃嗎？"男人又問。

"很好吃。"海生的朋友開心地說。

幾個男人又笑了："好，那我們今天也吃麵。去做吧。"

海生想，要是爸爸知道了會生氣。

可是，他也很開心：這是他第一次在飯店裡做面！

57　生氣 (shēngqì) vo., adj. to get angry; angry

58　第一次 (dì-yī cì) phrase first time

"小朋友，我喜歡你的面。"吃完
₅₉ ₁₉ ₃₅

面，一個男人對海生說。"多少錢?"

"我不知道……"海生看看那個男
₄₆

人，笑了："給多少都行。"
₅₀ ₆₀

---

59 小朋友 (xiǎopéngyou) *n.* kid   **60** 行 (xíng) *adj.* all right

"我們會再來的。"給了錢，幾個男

人走了出去。

　過了一會兒，又來了幾個人。海生

又做了面，大家都很喜歡吃他做的面。

可是，吃完以後，每個人給的錢都不

一樣，誰都不知道要給多少錢。

61　一會兒 (yīhuìr) *tn.* a little while

62　大家 (dàjiā) *n.* everyone

63　不一樣 (bù yīyàng) *phrase* not the same

Three

很開心

晚上七點左右, 老周和周太太回到
了飯店, 看到幾個人在吃麵。海生和
他的一個朋友在看書。

"海生, 這面……面是哪兒來的?"

老周問, 聽起來有一點生氣。

"爸爸, 媽媽, 面是我做的。"

---

64 左右 (zuǒyòu) *phrase* about, approximately

65 看書 (kànshū) *vo.* to read, to study

66 聽起來 (tīng qǐlai) *vc.* to sound…

67 有一點 (yǒu yīdiǎn) *phrase* to be a little (too)

海生說。"你們下午都不在，有人

來吃飯，可是，他們點的菜我都不會

做。可是，我會做面。"

　　"兒子，你什麼時候會做面了？"

---

68 點菜 (diǎncài) *vo.* to order food　　**69** 時候 (shíhou) *n.* when

周太太聽起來很開心。

"今天是我第一次做。"海生一邊

寫字一邊說。

"面怎麼樣?還可以吧?"老周走過

去,一個一個問吃麵的人。

知道了大家都很喜歡海生做的面,

老周不那麼生氣了,他問:"海生,你

知道這個面多少錢嗎?"

"我也不知道,每個人給的錢都不

一樣。"

---

70 過去 (guòqu) *vc.* to go over   72 那麼 (nàme) *adv.* so (much)

71 一個一個 (yī gè yī gè) *adv.* one by one

"這怎麼行？要是有人吃完以後說，你做的面不好吃，不給錢……"老周說。

海生不說話了。

可是，沒有一個人不喜歡吃海生做的面。

第二天中午，飯店裡來了很多人。有的點了菜和飯，有人要點海生做的面。

"海生去上學了。"周太太對人們笑

笑，"面，我叫老周來做。"
50   2

"那不行，我們是來吃海生做的面
      48

的。"

"謝謝大家那麼喜歡我兒子做的面。"
      62   72   19   10

周太太開心地說。
      39

吃過 "海生面" 的人都說好吃，有

人聽說好吃，來飯店吃飯的時候也會

點這個面。海生和他的家人都很開

心。

---

74 聽說 (tīngshuō) *v.* to hear tell, to hear   **75** 家人 (jiārén) *n.* family member(s)
said (that)

送菜

Four

下午四點

　　一天下午，一個老太太來飯店對周
太太說："我晚上不想做飯了，你叫
老周給我做幾個菜，晚上五點半左
右送到我家。到時候，我再給錢。行
吧？"

　　"可以的，錢太太。"周太太說。

---

76 老太太 (lǎotàitai) *n.* old lady

77 做飯 (zuò fàn) *vo.* to cook a meal

78 送到 (sòngdào) *vc.* to send to

79 到時候 (dào shíhou) *phrase* when the time comes

錢太太走了以後，又來了一個女
<u>的</u>，三十歲左右，也很好看。

"馬老師，你來了。今天要吃點什
麼?" 周太太走過去問。

"周太太，今天我不能在飯店裡吃。

好看 (hǎokàn) *adj.* good-looking

我過來點一個菜，還有'海生面'。晚

上七點左右能不能送到我家來?"

"可以的。"

"謝 謝周太太。"馬老師開心地笑

了笑，"錢給你，我走了。"

周太太對老周說："錢太太和馬老

師點的東西，晚上我去送吧。"

"要是你出去的話，我一個人不行

的。叫海生去送吧。"老周一邊做菜一

邊說。

---

81 過來 (guòlai) *vc.* to come over   **83** 一個人 (yī gè rén) *phrase* alone

82 送 (sòng) *v.* to send, to deliver

"怎麼能叫小朋友去送?"

"可以的，海生都八歲了。"老周

對太太笑了笑。

下午四點多，海生回來了。周太太

對兒子說：“海生，你寫字寫完了嗎？”

“還沒。”海生說。

“錢太太和馬老師點了菜，今天晚上你給她們送過去。”

“知道了。”海生還在寫字。

Five

下午五點

五點左右,周太太給兒子做了吃的。
<u>64</u>　　　　　　<u>10</u>　　　　　<u>31</u>

海生吃完以後, 錢太太的菜也做完了。
　　<u>35</u>　<u>33</u>

"錢太太要我們五點半送到。"周太
　　　　　　　　　<u>78</u>

太對兒子說, "你小心點。"
<u>10</u>　　　　　<u>84</u>

"知道了。"

"海生!"一個小朋友說。"你去哪
　　　　　　　　<u>59</u>

兒?"海生的好朋友明明走了過來。
　　　　　　　　　　　<u>85</u>

---

84 小心點 (xiǎoxīn diǎn) *phrase* to be (more) careful

85 走了過來 (zǒu le guòlai) *phrase* walked over

"我去送東西。有人點了我家的菜。"

海生說。"你去哪兒?"

"那邊有很多小朋友，不知道他們

在做什麼。我們一起去看看吧!"

"好，去看看。"

他們和小朋友一起說,一起笑,很開

心。

"明明，都五點半了。走，回家吃

飯了。"明明的媽媽走過來說。

"什麼? 都五點半了?"海生說。"錢

太太的東西還沒送到。" 他一邊說一

邊走。

　　"小心點！有車！"明明的媽媽對海

生說。

晚上六點

六點，海生到了錢太太家。

"對不起，錢太太，我來晚了一點。
這是你要的菜。"錢太太開門的時候，
海生說。

"怎麼是你送來的?"錢太太笑了一
下，看了一下海生手裡的菜，"海生，

---

88 對不起 (duìbuqǐ) *phrase* I'm sorry

89 開門 (kāimén) *vo.* to open the door

90 一下 (yīxià) *adv.* briefly, for a second

91 手裡 (shǒu lǐ) *phrase* in one's hand

菜怎麼會這樣……"
<u>43</u> <u>92</u>

"<u>對不起</u>，我<u>走過來</u>的。"
88 87

"<u>行吧</u>，謝謝你！這錢是給你爸爸
60

媽媽的。"

"不用謝。"說完，海生又走回了飯
店。

"東西送到了嗎?"周太太問。

"送到了。這是錢太太給的錢。"海
生一邊說，一邊給媽媽錢。

"好兒子。過一會兒,還有一個要送。"

Seven

晚上六點半

六點半<u>左右</u>, 馬老師的菜和麵都做
完了。

周太太<u>對</u>兒子說:"馬老師給<u>過</u>錢
了。她家在錢太太家<u>後面</u>一點。<u>那邊</u>
有一個小門,到了<u>以後</u>,第二個門是馬
老師家。"

"知道了。"海生<u>又</u>走了<u>出去</u>。

海生到了小門，走到第三家的門

邊，開門的人是一個男人。

"這是你要的面和菜。"海生說。

"謝謝你。"男人說。"這是給你

的。"男人一邊說，一邊給錢。

"謝謝。再見。"

"再見。"

"不對，媽媽說，馬老師給過錢了。為什麼那個男人還給我錢? 他是誰……" 海生又走了回去。

開門的還是那個男人。"你好，小朋友，你怎麼回來了?"

"對不起，這裡是馬老師的家嗎?" 海生問。

"不是，馬老師家是第二家。" 男人說。

---

95 回去 (huíqu) *vc.* to go back

"對不起，我的東西是要送到馬老師家的。"

"可是，東西你都給我了，錢我也給你了。"男人說完笑了。

"你怎麼能這樣？我叫馬老師來。"海生一邊說，一邊去叫馬老師。馬老師開門，和海生一起走了過來。

"你好，這個小朋友送的東西是我點的。我給她媽媽錢了。"

"馬老師,你好。"男人第一次見到馬老師，他不知道馬老師這麼好看。"對

對對，這個<u>小朋友</u>也跟我說了。你
₅₉

看<u>這樣</u><u>行</u><u>不行</u>，今天的<u>晚飯</u>，我們一
₉₂ ₆₀ ₄₈ ₉₆

<u>起</u>吃吧。我給你錢。"
₁₄

　　<u>馬</u>老師<u>聽</u>完<u>笑</u>了："<u>行</u>吧。那謝謝
₂₅ ₅₀ ₆₀

你。"

---

96 晚飯 (wǎnfàn) *n.* dinner

"不用謝。"男人也笑了，"小朋

友，我給你的錢，你給馬老師吧。"

"好。對不起，下次不會這樣了。"海

生說。

"回去吧。"馬老師說。

"謝謝你，小朋友。"男人說。

"謝謝。再見。"海生走了。

海生回到飯店沒說什麼，老周和周

太太想："他做得很好。"過了幾天，錢

太太和馬老師又來飯店點菜，還問周

---

97 下次 (xià cì) *tn.* next time

98 過了幾天 (guò le jǐ tiān) *phrase* after a few days had passed

太太，為什麼叫海生去送菜。

聽她們說完，周太太說："對不起，

他太小了，下次不叫他送了。"

山東飯店

Eight

學那個小朋友

晚上, 老周對太太說:"今年這裡開飯店的人多了。上個月又開了一個山東飯店。那家飯店門邊, 每天都有一個小朋友在說山東飯店的菜好吃。"

"我聽到了, 有的人想要來我們家, 可是都去他們家了。"周太太聽起來

---

99 開飯店 (kāi fàndiàn) *vo.* to open a restaurant

100 上個月 (shàng ge yuè) *tn.* last month

101 聽到 (tīngdào) *vc.* to hear

很不開心，"那，你想怎麼做?"
<u>102</u>   <u>52</u>

"海生送菜送不好,叫他做這個吧。"
  <u>82</u>   <u>82</u>   <u>2</u>

老周說。

"可以叫他做做看。"
   <u>2</u>

---

102 不開心 (bù kāixīn) *phrase* not happy, to
be unhappy

第二天下午，海生回來以後，周太
太叫他去山東飯店門邊看看。

海生看過回來說："那家店門邊有
一個小朋友，跟我一樣大，他在叫人
去他家飯店吃飯。"

"他家飯店裡人多嗎?" 周太太問。

"多，他家飯店裡的人很多。"

"那好，你也要學那個小朋友那樣，
叫人來我們家飯店吃飯。"

海生走出飯店，聽見山東飯店的

---

103 一樣 (yīyàng) *n.* the same
104 那樣 (nàyàng) *adv.* like that
105 走出 (zǒuchū) *vc.* to walk out
106 聽見 (tīngjiàn) *vc.* to hear

小朋友在叫："大家好，我爸爸是山

東人，做的都是好吃的山東菜。來來

來，不好吃不要錢。"

　　那個小朋友很會說，可是海生一下

107 很會說 (hěn huì shuō) *phrase* is a smooth talker

108 一下子 (yīxiàzi) *adv.* all of a sudden; all at once

子不知道說什麼。周太太出來跟兒子
108   109   10

說了一下，走了。
      90

---

109 出來 (chūlai) *vc.* to come out

Nine

都好吃

"大家好，我爸爸是山西人。"海生
62

說，"他做的都是好吃的山西菜。山
3

東菜不好吃，來吃山西菜吧，不好吃
3   3

不要錢。"說完，海生開心地笑了。
49   39   50

可是，山東飯店的小朋友聽到以後
6   5   59   101   33

很生氣。
57

"你怎麼能說這樣的話？"他一邊
52   92   40

走一邊生氣地說。

"我喜歡這樣說!"

"你可以說山西菜好吃，可是你不

能說山東菜不好吃!" 山東飯店的小

朋友大叫。

"我還是要說！"海生生氣地說。

"好，那我也這樣說。"山東飯店

的小朋友回到飯店門邊說："來來來，

好吃的山東菜，人人都喜歡，不好吃

不要錢。山西飯店的菜不好吃，誰都

不喜歡！"

海生聽山東飯店的小朋友這樣說，生

氣地走了過去，大叫："你不可以這

樣說！"

一個老人走過來，看看海生，又看

---

112 老人 (lǎorén) *n.* old person, old man

看山東飯店的小朋友。

海生看看老人說：“山東菜不好吃，來吃山西菜吧，我爸爸做的都是好吃的山西菜。”

山東飯店的小朋友很生氣，也看看老人說：“來來來，好吃的山東菜，人人都喜歡，山西飯店的菜不好吃，誰都不喜歡！”

“不對，不對，你說的不對！”海生說，他很生氣。

“你的話也不對！”山東飯店的

小朋友說。
59

　他們都在大叫，都很生氣。
　　　　　111　　　　　57

　老人左看看，右看看，不知道去哪
　112　46　　　46

個飯店。老人聽他們這樣說，也很不
　5　　112　25　　　　92

開心，走了。
102

　老人走了以後，他們都不說話了。
　112　　　33　　　　　　20

海生看看山東飯店的小朋友說:"他沒去你們飯店,也沒有來我們飯店。"

"他不喜歡我們這樣做,可是,我家飯店做的菜很好吃。"山東飯店的小朋友說,他有一點不開心。

"你們飯店的菜我吃過,很好吃。可是我們飯店的菜也很好吃。"海生也有一點不開心。

可是老人沒有去山東飯店也沒有去山西飯店,他走了。

Ten

和你一樣

那天以後，海生和山東飯店的小朋
友還是會在飯店門邊，叫人去吃飯。可
是，他們不說不好聽的話了。

海生和山東飯店的小朋友是好朋友
了。

要是有人走到飯店門邊，他們會一
起說：

---

113 那天 (nà tiān) *tn.* that day

114 不好聽 (bù hǎotīng) *phrase* unpleasant-sounding

"不用去山東，也不用去山西，來我們飯店，你可以吃好吃的菜！"

要是有人在山西飯店門邊，想吃麵，海生會說："山東飯店的面也很好吃。"

要是有人在山東飯店門邊，想吃麵，山東飯店的小朋友也會說："山西飯店的海生面也很好吃。"

喜歡周家飯店的人還是很多，喜歡山東飯店的人也多了。

周太太看兒子做得這麼好，對老周

說：“以後，叫兒子也和你一樣，開飯
　　 33　　 2　 10　　　　　103
店。”
99

　“他這麼小，誰知道他以後要做什
　　　 22　　　　　　　 33
麼？

"你說得對，要看他喜不喜歡。"

"我看他是有一點喜歡的。他有時候會看我做菜，還喜歡問我怎麼開一個好飯店，怎麼做菜，怎麼跟來吃飯的人說話。"

"兒子跟你學了不少東西。"周太太笑得很開心。

"要是他以後也開飯店，那他跟我學的東西，都是很有用的!"老周也開心地笑了。

---

115 要看 (yào kàn) *phrase* to depend on⋯   117 有用 (yǒuyòng) *adj.* useful
116 有時候 (yǒu shíhou) *phrase* sometimes

Key Words 關鍵詞 (Guānjiàncí)

1. 歲 suì *mw.* years old
2. 叫 jiào *v.* to be called, to call; to tell (someone to do something)
3. 好吃 hǎochī *adj.* tasty
4. 家 jiā *mw.* measure word for shops
5. 飯店 fàndiàn *n.* restaurant
6. 可是 kěshì *conj.* but
7. 還 hái *adv.* still
8. 老家 lǎojiā *n.* hometown
9. 太太 tàitai *n.* wife, lady, Mrs.
10. 兒子 érzi *n.* son
11. 出生 chūshēng *v.* to be born
12. 名字 míngzi *n.* name
13. 的時候 de shíhou *phrase* when⋯
14. 一起 yìqǐ *adv.* together
15. 一家人 yì jiā rén *phrase* the whole family
16. 晚 wǎn *adj.* late
17. 關門 guānmén *vo.* to close shop, to close a door
18. 回家 huíjiā *vo.* to go home
19. 喜歡 xǐhuan *v.* to like
20. 說話 shuōhuà *vo.* to speak (words), to talk
21. 生日 shēngrì *n.* birthday
22. 這麼 zhème *adv.* so⋯
23. 天天 tiāntiān *adv.* every day
24. 上學 shàngxué *vo.* to start school, to go to school
25. 聽 tīng *v.* to listen (to)
26. 點點頭 diǎndian tóu *phrase* to (briefly) nod one's head

27. 小時候 xiǎo shíhou *phrase* when one was little
28. 開心 kāixīn *adj.* happy
29. 中午 zhōngwǔ *n.* noon
30. 早上 zǎoshang *tn.* morning
31. 吃的 chī de *n.* food
32. 午飯 wǔfàn *n.* lunch
33. 以後 yǐhòu *adv.* after; later, in the future
34. 在一起 zài yīqǐ *phrase* to be together
35. 吃完 chī wán *vc.* to finish eating
36. 又 yòu *adv.* again
37. 東西 dōngxi *n.* thing(s), stuff
38. 要是 yàoshi *conj.* if
39. 開心地 kāixīn de *phrase* happily
40. 一邊 yībiān *conj.* while doing... (two things)
41. 門邊 mén biān *phrase* by the door
42. 看到 kàndào *vc.* to see
43. 怎麼會 zěnme huì *phrase* how could
44. 回來 huílai *vc.* to come back
45. 還是 háishi *conj., adv.* still
46. 看看 kànkan *v.* to take a look
47. 再 zài *adv.* again (in the future)
48. 不行 bù xíng *phrase* not OK
49. 說完 shuō wán *vc.* to finish speaking
50. 笑 xiào *v.* to laugh, to smile
51. 做面 zuò miàn *vo.* to make noodles
52. 怎麼 zěnme *adv.* how
53. 這時候 zhè shíhou *phrase* at this time
54. 出去 chūqu *vc.* to go out
55. 做菜 zuòcài *vo.* to cook food
56. 晚上 wǎnshang *tn.* evening
57. 生氣 shēngqì *vo., adj.* to get angry; angry
58. 第一次 dì-yī cì *phrase* first time
59. 小朋友 xiǎopéngyou *n.* kid
60. 行 xíng *adj.* all right
61. 一會兒 yīhuìr *tn.* a little while
62. 大家 dàjiā *n.* everyone

63. 不一樣 bù yīyàng *phrase* not the same
64. 左右 zuǒyòu *phrase* about, approximately
65. 看書 kànshū *vo.* to read, to study
66. 聽起來 tīng qǐlai *vc.* to sound···
67. 有一點 yǒu yīdiǎn *phrase* to be a little (too)
68. 點菜 diǎncài *vo.* to order food
69. 時候 shíhou *n.* when
70. 過去 guòqu *vc.* to go over
71. 一個一個 yī gè yī gè *adv.* one by one
72. 那麼 nàme *adv.* so (much)
73. 第二天 dì-èr tiān *phrase* the next day
74. 聽說 tīngshuō *v.* to hear tell, to hear said (that)
75. 家人 jiārén *n.* family member(s)
76. 老太太 lǎotàitai *n.* old lady
77. 做飯 zuò fàn *vo.* to cook a meal
78. 送到 sòngdào *vc.* to send to
79. 到時候 dào shíhou *phrase* when the time comes
80. 好看 hǎokàn *adj.* good-looking
81. 過來 guòlai *vc.* to come over
82. 送 sòng *v.* to send, to deliver
83. 一個人 yī gè rén *phrase* alone
84. 小心點 xiǎoxīn diǎn *phrase* to be (more) careful
85. 走了過來 zǒu le guòlai *phrase* walked over
86. 那邊 nàbiān *n.* over there
87. 走過來 zǒu guòlai *vc.* to walk over
88. 對不起 duìbuqǐ *phrase* I'm sorry
89. 開門 kāimén *vo.* to open the door
90. 一下 yīxià *adv.* briefly, for a second
91. 手裡 shǒu lǐ *phrase* in one's hand
92. 這樣 zhèyàng *pr.* like this
93. 不用謝 bùyòng xiè *phrase* You're welcome (lit. "no need to thank")
94. 後面 hòumian *n.* behind
95. 回去 huíqu *vc.* to go back
96. 晚飯 wǎnfàn *n.* dinner
97. 下次 xià cì *tn.* next time

98. 過了幾天 guò le jǐ tiān *phrase* after a few days had passed
99. 開飯店 kāi fàndiàn *vo.* to open a restaurant
100. 上個月 shàng ge yuè *tn.* last month
101. 聽到 tīngdào *vc.* to hear
102. 不開心 bù kāixīn *phrase* not happy, to be unhappy
103. 一樣 yíyàng *n.* the same
104. 那樣 nàyàng *adv.* like that
105. 走出 zǒuchū *vc.* to walk out
106. 聽見 tīngjiàn *vc.* to hear
107. 很會說 hěn huì shuō *phrase* is a smooth talker
108. 一下子 yíxiàzi *adv.* all of a sudden; all at once
109. 出來 chūlai *vc.* to come out
110. 生氣地 shēngqì de *phrase* angrily
111. 大叫 dà jiào *v.* to call out loudly
112. 老人 lǎorén *n.* old person, old man
113. 那天 nà tiān *tn.* that day
114. 不好聽 bù hǎotīng *phrase* unpleasant-sounding
115. 要看 yào kàn *phrase* to depend on···
116. 有時候 yǒu shíhou *phrase* sometimes
117. 有用 yǒuyòng *adj.* useful

Part of Speech Key

adj.	Adjective	*prep.*	Preposition
adv.	Adverb	*pr.*	Pronoun
aux.	Auxiliary Verb	*pn.*	Proper noun
conj.	Conjunction	*tn.*	Time Noun
cov.	Coverb	*v.*	Verb
mw.	Measure word	*vc.*	Verb plus complement
n.	Noun	*vo.*	Verb plus object
on.	Onomatopoeia		
part.	Particle		

Grammar Points

For learners new to reading Chinese, an understanding of grammar points can be extremely helpful for learners and teachers. The following is a list of the most challenging grammar points used in this graded reader.

These grammar points correspond to the Common European Framework of Reference for Languages (CEFR) level A2 or above. The full list with explanations and examples of each grammar point can be found on the Chinese Grammar Wiki, the definitive source of information on Chinese grammar online.

ENGLISH	CHINESE
CHAPTER 1	
Indicating location with "zai" before verbs	Subj. + 在 + Place + Verb
Directional verbs "lai" and "qu"	來 / 去 + Place
After a specific time with "yihou"	Time / Verb + 以後
In the future in general with "yihou"	以後, ……
Reduplication of verbs	Verb + Verb
Expressing "and also" with "hai"	還 + Verb
Expressing "when" with "de shihou"	……的時候
Adjectives with "name" and "zheme"	那麼 / 這麼 + Adj.
Expressing "together" with "yiqi"	一起 + Verb
Two words for "but"	……, 可是 / 但是……
Emphasizing quantity with "dou"	大家 / 很多人 + 都……

Expressing "a little too" with "you yidian"	有一點 (兒) + Adj.
Result complements "-dao" and "-jian"	Verb + 到 / 見
Moderating positive adjectives with "hai"	還 + Adj.
Using "youde" to mean "some"	有的 + Noun
Expressing "had better" with "haishi"	還是 + Verb
The "shi... de" construction for indicating purpose	是……的
Expressing "one by one" with "yi"	一 + Measure Word + 一 + Measure Word
Expressing experiences with "guo"	Verb + 過

CHAPTER 4

Causative verbs	Subj. + 讓 / 叫 / 請 / 使 + Person + Predicate
Indicating a number in excess	Number + 多
Direction complement	Verb (+ Direction) + 來 / 去

CHAPTER 5

| Expressing "already" with "dou" | 都 + Time + 了 |

CHAPTER 6

| Comparing "youdian" and "yidian" | 有點 vs. 一點 |
| Conceding with "ba" | ……吧 |

CHAPTER 8

| Expressing "all at once" with "yixiazi" | Subj. + 一下子 + Verb + 了 |

CHAPTER 9

| Expressing "to come from" with "laizi" | Subj. + 來自 + Place |
| Expressing "a little too" with "you dian" | 有點 (兒) + Adj. |

CHAPTER 10

Basic comparisons with "yiyang"	Noun 1 + 跟 / 和 + Noun 2 + 一樣 + Adj.
In the future in general with "yihou"	以後, ……

Credits

Story Authors : John Pasden, Jared Turner
Editor-in-Chief : John Pasden
Content Editor : Chen Shishuang
Editor : Li Jiong, Ma Lihua
Illustrator : Hu Sheng
Producer : Jared Turner

Acknowledgments

We are grateful to Ma Lihua, Li Jiong, Song Shen, Tan Rong, Chen Shishuang, and the entire team at AllSet Learning for working on this project and contributing the perfect mix of talent to produce this series.

Special thanks to Wang Hui and her 7th grade Chinese dual immersion class at Adele C. Young Intermediate School for being our test readers: AJ Bushnell, Brandon Murray, Colin Grunander, Emma Page, Isaak Diehl, Jackson Faerber, Jason Lee, Kyden Cefalo, Max Norton, Maxwell Isaacson, Olivia Barker, and Xavier Putnam. Also thanks to Aiden Benford, Heather Turner, Miles Turner, Jake Liu, Paris Yamamoto, and Rory O' Neill for being our test readers.

About Mandarin Companion

Mandarin Companion was started by Jared Turner and John Pasden, who met one fateful day on a bus in Shanghai when the only remaining seats forced them to sit next to each other.

John majored in Japanese in college in the US and later learned Mandarin before moving to China, where he was admitted into an all-Chinese masters program in applied linguistics at East China Normal University in Shanghai. John lives in Shanghai with his wife and children. John is the editor-in-chief at Mandarin Companion and ensures each story is written at the appropriate level.

Jared decided to move to China with his young family in search of career opportunities, despite having no Chinese language skills. When he learned about Extensive Reading and started using graded readers, his language skills exploded. In 3 months, he had read 10 graded readers and quickly became conversational in Chinese. Jared lives in the US with his wife and children. Jared runs the business operations and focuses on bringing stories to life.

John and Jared work with Chinese learners and teachers all over the world. They host a podcast, You Can Learn Chinese, where they discuss the struggles and joys of learning to speak the language. They are active on social media, where they share memes and stories about learning Chinese.

You can connect with them through the website
www.mandarincompanion.com

Other Stories from Mandarin Companion

Breakthrough Readers: 150 Characters

My Teacher Is a Martian
《我的老師是火星人》
by John Pasden, Jared Turner

Xiao Ming, Boy Sherlock
《小明》
by John Pasden, Jared Turner

In Search of Hua Ma
《花馬》
by John Pasden, Jared Turner

Just Friends?
《我們是朋友嗎?》
by John Pasden, Jared Turner

Level 1 Readers: 300 Characters

The Secret Garden
《秘密花園》
by Frances Hodgson Burnett

The Sixty Year Dream
《六十年的夢》
by Washington Irving

The Monkey's Paw
《猴爪》
by W. W. Jacobs

The Country of the Blind
《盲人國》
by H. G. Wells

Sherlock Holmes and the Case of the Curly-Haired Company
《捲髮公司的案子》
by Sir Arthur Conan Doyle

The Prince and the Pauper
《王子和窮孩子》
by Mark Twain

Emma
《安末》
by Jane Austen

The Ransom of Red Chief
《紅猴的價格》
by O. Henry

Level 2 Readers: 450 Characters

Great Expectations: Part 1
《美好的前途（上）》
  by Charles Dickens

Great Expectations: Part 2
《美好的前途（下）》
  by Charles Dickens

Journey to the Center of the Earth
《地心遊記》
  by Jules Verne

Jekyll and Hyde
《江可和黑德》
  by Robert Louis Stevenson

Mandarin companion is producing a growing library of graded readers for Chinese language learners.

Visit our website for the newest books available:

WWW.MANDARINCOMPANION.COM

Printed in the USA
CPSIA information can be obtained
at www.ICGtesting.com
LVHW081748031123
762986LV00046B/1085

9 781941 875414